Activity Manual

Third Edition

bju press®

Greenville, South Carolina

Note
The fact that materials produced by other publishers may be referred to in
this volume does not constitute an endorsement of the content or theological
position of materials produced by such publishers. Any references and ancillary
materials are listed as an aid to the student or the teacher and in an attempt to
maintain the accepted academic standards of the publishing industry.

HERITAGE STUDIES 2 Activity Manual
Third Edition

Authors
Eileen Berry
Gina Bradstreet
Ann Larson

Bible Integration
Bryan Smith

Consultants
Dottie Buckley
Jim Davis
Katie Klipp

Permissions
Sylvia Gass
Kathleen Thompson
Carrie Walker

Project Editor
Carolyn Cooper

Page Layout
Bonnijean Marley

Book Designer
Michael Asire

Cover Design
Elly Kalagayan

Cover Art
Ben Schipper

Cover Photography
Craig Oesterling

Illustrators
Paula Cheadle
Preston Gravely
Kathy Pflug
Dave Schuppert
Lynda Slattery
Courtney Godbey Wise

Project Coordinator
Kendra Wright Winchester

Photograph credits appear on page 203.

© 2014 BJU Press
Greenville, South Carolina 29614
First Edition © 1979 BJU Press
Second Editon © 1996 BJU Press

ISBN 978-1-60682-472-6

15 14 13 12 11 10 9 8 7 6 5 4

Contents

Dear Parent,

We are pleased to provide a comprehensive Heritage Studies program developed from the perspective of a Christian worldview. The Activity Manual accompanies the *Heritage Studies 2 Student Text* and is an integral part of the Heritage Studies 2 program.

The Activity Manual pages provide reinforcement of the skills taught in the Heritage Studies 2 materials and aid the teacher in evaluating each student's grasp of the concepts presented in the lessons. The pages include Bible connections, geography and map skill practice, study skills, and chapter reviews. Instructions for use of the Activity Manual are found in the *Heritage Studies 2 Teacher's Edition*.

As a parent there are many ways you can support and enhance your child's interest in and knowledge of history. Reading with your child is one vital way. The following trade book titles have been selected to correspond to your child's grade level and social studies themes in these materials. The following JourneyForth titles are available from BJU Press. To place an order, visit www.bjupress.com/books/journeyforth.

JourneyForth Titles

Haiku on Your Shoe
Mumsi Meets a Lion

What God Made

Circle the word that names something God made.

1. tractor   horse

2. tree   house

3. ball   sun

4. ocean   swimming pool

5. man   doll

6. lamp   star

Circle those that are made in God's image.

7. tree   baby   man   dog

Circle the pictures that show how you can care for God's world.

Glue the correct picture beside the "cause" to show the "effect."

Cause	Effect

1. If you leave a book outside on a cloudy day,

2. If you leave your bike in the driveway,

3. If you eat too much at one time,

4. If you tip your chair,

Cause & Effect

Cut along the solid lines.

Continents

Africa   Asia   Europe   North   South

Write the missing names on the map.

The big areas of land are continents, and the large bodies of water are oceans. There are seven continents and four oceans.

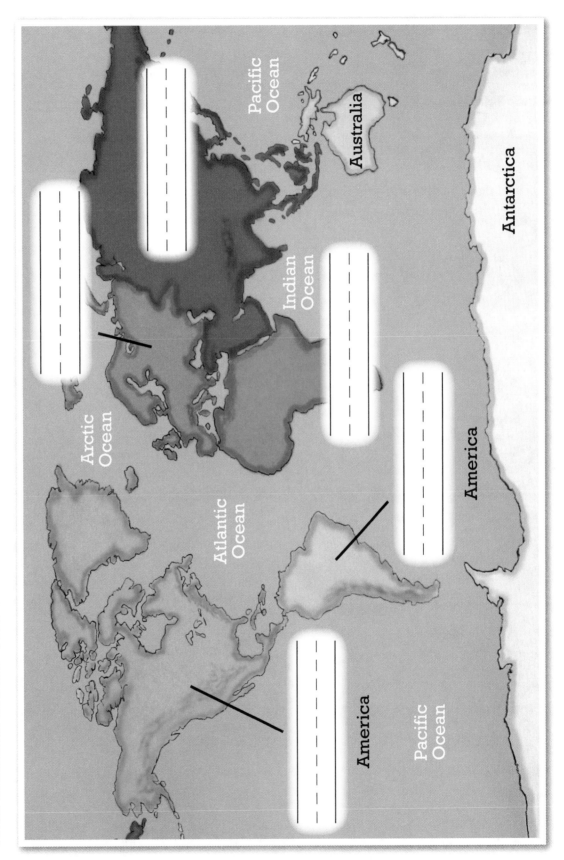

Pacific
Ocean

Australia

Antarctica

Indian
Ocean

Arctic
Ocean

Atlantic
Ocean

America

America

Pacific
Ocean

HERITAGE
STUDIES

The Zoo

Use the compass rose to complete each sentence.

1. The monkeys are _____ of the turtles.

2. The alligators are _____ of the zebras.

3. The turtles are _____ of the monkeys.

4. The zebras are _____ of the alligators.

Compass Rose

The **compass rose** shows directions on the map.

Animals in the Zoo

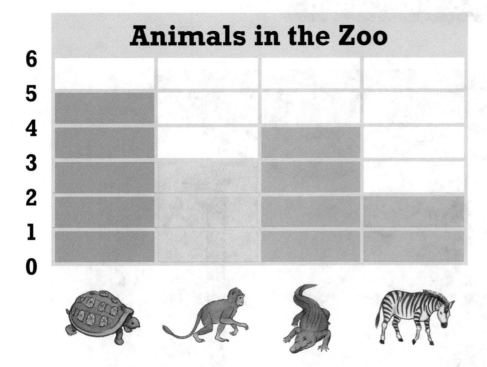

Use the bar graph to find the correct answer. Circle the correct picture.

5. Does the zoo have more turtles or zebras?

6. Does the zoo have fewer monkeys or alligators?

7. Which animal is shown by the blue bar?

Places on a Globe

Equator, North Pole, and South Pole

The top of the globe is called the **North Pole**. The bottom of the globe is called the **South Pole**. The **equator** is the line around the widest part of the globe.

Follow the directions.

1. Trace a red line along the equator.

2. Color the continent north of the equator green.

3. Color the continent that the equator runs through orange.

4. Color the North Pole purple.

5. Color the South Pole red.

6. Color the oceans blue.

North

West —— East

South

Adoniram & Ann Judson

Mark the correct answer.
You may use your book.

1. Where did the Judsons go?

   ○ China   ○ Burma

2. What did the Judsons build?

   ○ a house of bricks   ○ a house of bamboo

3. What did Adoniram put into the Burmese language?

   ○ the Bible   ○ a poem

4. Who kept the Burmese Bible safe?

   ○ a Burmese friend   ○ God

5. Mark the word written in Burmese.

   ○ Bible   ○ ခရစ်ယာန်ကျမ်းစာ

Complete the sentence.

6. The Judsons learned the Burmese language because

   _

_____

_ _ _ _ _ _ _ _ _ _ _ _ ⭐

Circle the correct answer.

1. Who did God make in His own image?

2. Who does God love?

3. Who is obeying the rule?

4. Which people are filling the earth?

5. Which children are speaking the same language?

Use the map to complete the page.

6. Trace the equator purple.

7. Color North America green.

8. Color the oceans blue.

9. Draw a boat south of the equator.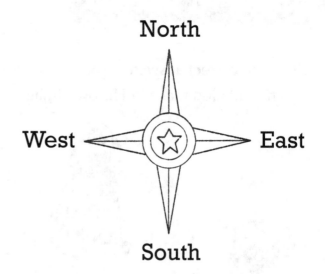

10. Color the part of the compass rose pointing north red.

HERITAGE STUDIES

_____

– – – – – – – – – – – – – – – –

_____

Follow the directions.

1. Circle the names of two sons of Adam and Eve.

   Cain   Abel   Job

2. Circle the picture of the animals Abel cared for.

3. Circle the picture of Cain's offering.

4. Circle the picture that shows what Cain's community could have looked like.

5. Mark the phrases that explain what people in Cain's community did.

   ○ took care of animals   ○ used iron to make tools

   ○ built cars   ○ played music

Complete the sentence.

6. What are some things people do in your community?

   _____

   –

In my community people _____

_____

   –

_____

   –

_____.

Types of Communities

Communities

An **urban** community is in a city. A **suburb** is a community near a city but away from the busy part. A **rural** community is far from a city.

Mark all that apply to each kind of community.

Descriptions	Urban	Suburb	Rural
people live close together			
houses are far apart			
made up mostly of houses			
taxis and buses are used for transportation			
grow food or raise animals			
"the country"			
tall office buildings and stores			
farms and ranches			

Follow the directions.

1. Circle the kind of community you live in.   urban   suburb   rural

Complete the sentence.

2. What is your community like?

My community is _____

_____

_____

_____.

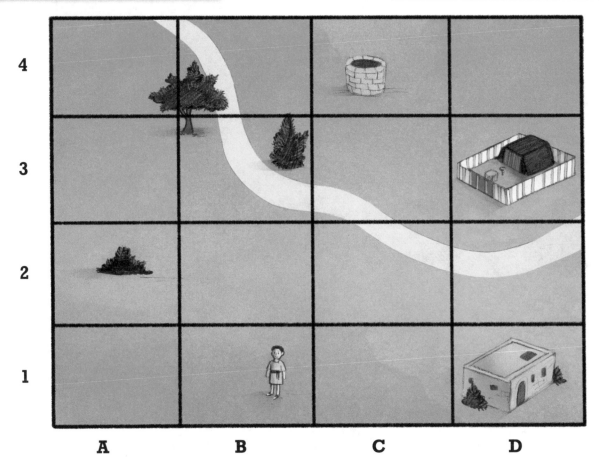

Map Grid
A **map grid** is a map made up of lines that form squares to help you locate places.

Mark the correct answer.

1. What is located in A2? ○ a bush ○ a tree

2. What is located in C4? ○ a well ○ a man

3. What is located in D1? ○ a river ○ a house

4. Where is the temple located? ○ D3 ○ A1

5. Where is the boy located? ○ C4 ○ B1

Circle the correct bold word.

Consumer and Producer

A person who makes, grows, or sells goods is a **producer**. If you buy or use the goods, you are a **consumer**.

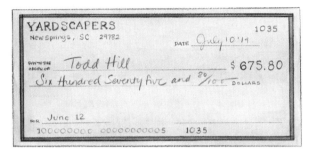

1. Mark is ready for a snack. Is a snack a **need** or a **want**?

2. Dad gets paid on Friday. Is his pay a **gift** or an **income**?

3. Mom goes to the store to buy some milk. Is Mom a **consumer** or a **producer**?

4. The baker is taking a tray of bread out of the oven. Is the baker a **consumer** or a **producer**?

5. Dad saves part of his pay. Is Dad at a **bank** or a **store**?

6. Luke hopes he gets a new bike for his birthday. Is a new bike a **need** or a **want**?

Volunteers

Write the word to complete the sentence.

What does a volunteer firefighter do?

Volunteer
A **volunteer** serves others without getting paid.

9-1-1
free
fire

He gives his services for
_____
_ _ _ _ _
_____ .

He can be reached by
_____
_ _ _ _ _
calling _____ .

He gets to a
_____
_ _ _ _ _
_____
as fast as he can.

Write the word that best completes the sentence.

> neighbor
>
> school
>
> zoo

_____

1. Liz likes to help children learn. She will volunteer at a _____.

2. Dan likes animals. He will volunteer at the _____.

3. Joe likes to help people. He will volunteer to help a _____.

> food bank
>
> hospital
>
> day care

4. Lily wants to be a nurse when she grows up.

   _____

   She wants to volunteer at a _____.

5. Jake wants to help hungry people. He will volunteer at a

   _____

   _____

6. Jill loves to help her mother bake cookies. They will volunteer

   _____

   to bake cookies for a _____.

‒ ‒ ‒ ‒ ‒ ‒ ‒ ‒ ‒ ‒ ‒ ‒

Complete the crossword puzzle.

Across

3. someone in charge of others

Down

1. the leader of a city or town

2. money paid to a government

3. rules that the people in a community must follow

laws   mayor
leader   taxes

Mayor

A **mayor** is the leader of a city or town.

Write a law or rule. Draw a picture of someone breaking the law or rule and someone obeying it.

Communities Change

Mark what Mayor Giuliani did to help New York City.

○ 1. did not panic

○ 2. helped people feel safe again

○ 3. made poor choices

○ 4. did not help police get their jobs done

○ 5. made wise choices

Answer the question.

6. How do you know Mr. Giuliani was a good mayor?

_____

_____

_____

_____

Write four ways the city in the picture has changed over time.

_____

7. _____

_____

8. _____

_____

9. _____

_____

10. _____

Chapter 2 Review

Follow the directions.

1. Circle the picture of a community today.

2. Circle the person that is volunteering.

3. Circle the urban or city community.

4. Circle the mayor making laws for the city.

5. Circle something a boy needs.

6. Circle the town that has changed over time.

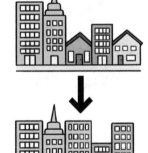

7. Mark two people that are **working** in their communities.

○ ○ ○

8. Mark two people that are **serving** in their communities.

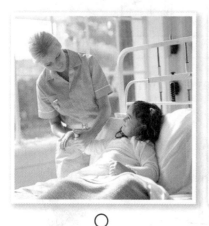  

○ ○ ○

9. Mark two people that are **volunteering** in their communities.

○ ○ ○

HERITAGE STUDIES ②

God's Kind of Leader

Flow Chart

A **flow chart** can show how things change over time.

Glue the pictures in the order in which the events happened or will happen.

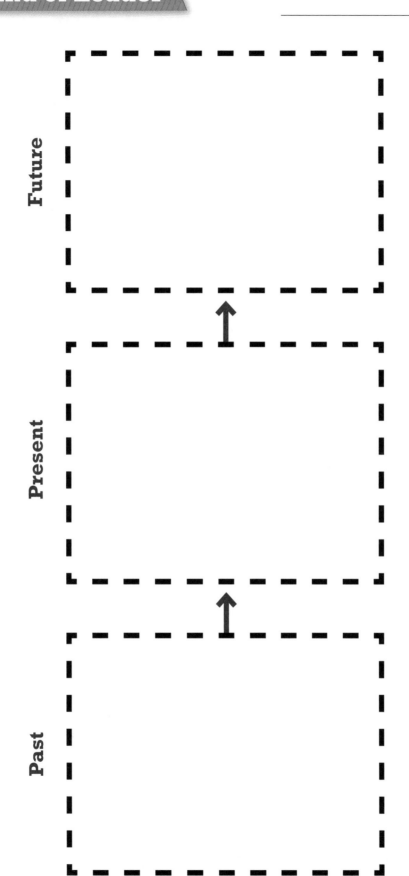

Past

Present

Future

Use your textbook to complete the sentence.

God wants leaders to be _____.

Cut along the solid lines.

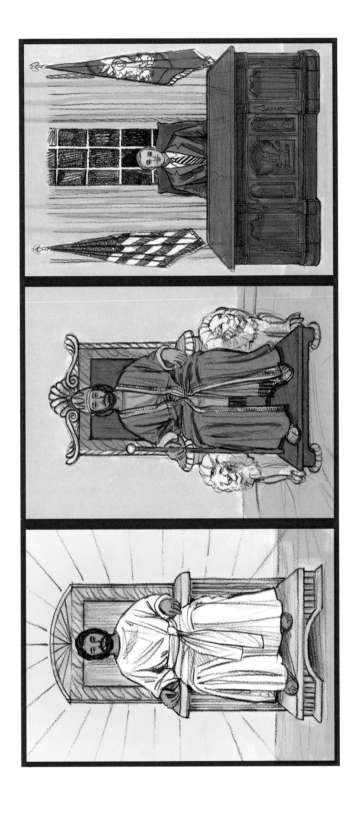

Your Three Governments

Use your textbook to find the answers.
Write the name of the leaders on the chart.
Glue the building under the correct heading.

| governor | mayor | president |

Governments

National	State	Local
_____ - - - - - - - - - _____	_____ - - - - - - - - - _____	_____ - - - - - - - - - _____

Cut along the solid lines.

What Governments Do

Use your textbook to complete the sentence about the right that allows these people to do these things.

Government

The **government** is a group of citizens chosen to lead a community, state, or country.

1. Citizens can _____
   _ _ _ _ _ _
   what they believe.

2. Citizens can _____
   _ _ _ _ _ _
   freely about anything.

Circle the sentence that shows how the law protects citizens.

3. Dogs are not allowed in the park.

   I can play because the dog is on a leash.

   My dog has a right to walk in the park.

The sign displays a community law.

Tax Money for Government Services

Schools	🏫 (image)
Roads	🛣 (image)
Parks	🪑 (image)

Key

tax dollar =

Pictograph

A **pictograph** uses pictures to show information.

Use the pictograph to find the answers.

_____
_ _ _ _ _ _ _ _
_____

4. Which service needs the most tax dollars?

_ _ _ _ _ _ _ _
_____

5. Which service needs the least tax dollars?

_ _ _ _ _ _ _ _
_____

6. Name the government service that needs 3 tax dollars.

Choosing Leaders

Circle the statements that you agree with.

Election

An **election** is choosing leaders by voting.

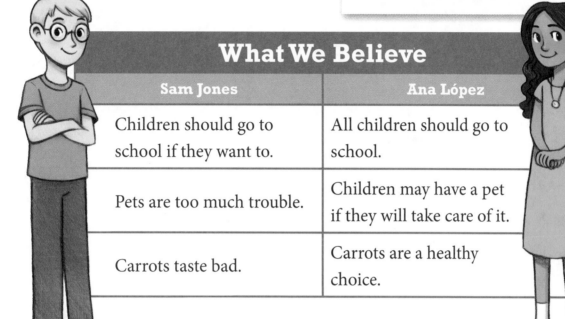

What We Believe

Sam Jones	Ana López
Children should go to school if they want to.	All children should go to school.
Pets are too much trouble.	Children may have a pet if they will take care of it.
Carrots taste bad.	Carrots are a healthy choice.

Vote by checking the name on the ballot.

Ballot

A **ballot** is a list of people wanting to be chosen as the leader.

VOTE

for the Grade 2 Leader

☐ **Sam Jones**

☐ **Ana López**

Complete the sentence.

I made my choice because _____ .

Circle the girl being responsible.
Put an *X* on the girl **not** being responsible.

Responsibility

A **responsibility** is something a citizen should do, such as obey the law.

What do you think the judge decided was just?

National Symbols

Match the meaning to each part of the Pledge of Allegiance.

Symbol

A **symbol** is a reminder of something important.

The Meaning of Our Pledge	
I pledge allegiance	I promise to be faithful
to the flag of the United States of America,	
and to the republic for which it stands,	
one nation under God,	
indivisible,	
with liberty and justice for all.	

Cut along the solid lines.

Glue the meaning beside the correct part of the Pledge.

to the American flag,	so that all are free and treated justly.
and the American citizens,	keeping citizens together,
a country under the rule of God,	

Anthem

A national **anthem** is a country's special song.

Underline the word or words in the song that have the same meaning as the word given.

1. morning — Oh, say can you see by the dawn's early light,

2. evening — What so proudly we hailed at the twilight's last gleaming?

3. war — Whose broad stripes and bright stars through the perilous fight,

4. walls of a fort — O'er the ramparts we watched were so gallantly streaming?

5. gunfire — And the rockets' red glare, the bombs bursting in air,

6. to show — Gave proof through the night that our flag was still there.

7. flag — Oh, say does that star-spangled banner yet wave

8. America — O'er the land of the free and the home of the brave?

HERITAGE STUDIES

Landmarks

Draw a line from the president to the landmark that represents him.

Landmark

A **landmark** is an important building or place.

1. George Washington

2. Thomas Jefferson

3. Abraham Lincoln

Citizens from Many Places

Glue the pictures in order.

Immigrants

Immigrants are people who move to a new country.

First

Second

Third

Last

Complete the sentence.

_____

— — — — — — — — — — — — — — — — — —

My ancestors are from _____.

Cut along the solid lines.

Chapter 3 Review

Underline the word that best completes the sentence.

1. God wants all leaders to be ____.

   tall

   just

   unfair

2. A ____ is a person who belongs to a certain place.

   congress

   government

   citizen

3. Leaders of a community, state, or country make up the ____.

   government

   consequences

   election

Mark the correct answer.

4. Citizens choose leaders by ____.

   ○ chance   ○ voting

5. Citizens are responsible to obey the ____.

   ○ law   ○ rights

6. Citizens should use their rights to ____ others.

   ○ help   ○ hurt

Follow the directions.

7. Circle the child standing correctly to say the Pledge of Allegiance.

8. Circle the man writing "The Star-Spangled Banner."

9. Circle the child following the law.

Circle the landmark.

10. Washington Monument

11. Jefferson Memorial

12. Lincoln Memorial

HERITAGE STUDIES

Using Natural Resources

Write ways we use each natural resource.

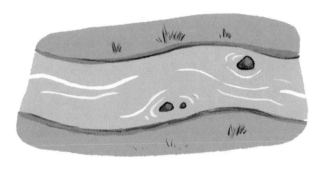

Natural Resource

A **natural resource** is something in nature that God gives people to use.

_____

_ _ _ _ _ _ _ _ _ _ _ _

_____

_____

_____

_ _ _ _ _ _ _ _ _ _ _ _

_____

_____

_____

_ _ _ _ _ _ _ _ _ _ _ _

_____

_ _ _ _ _ _ _ _ _ _ _ _

_____

_ _ _ _ _ _ _ _ _ _ _ _

_____

_ _ _ _ _ _ _ _ _ _ _ _

Regions & Weather

Draw a line to the region best suited for each worker.

farmland   forest   coast

Climate
The usual weather a region has in each season is called its **climate**.

Use the chart to find the correct weather symbols.

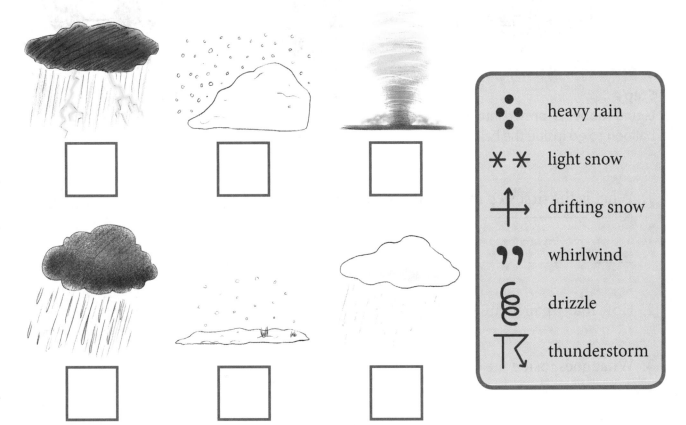

• • •	heavy rain
✶ ✶	light snow
↟	drifting snow
,,	whirlwind
⟆	drizzle
⟆⟍	thunderstorm

Soccer Ball Factory

Use the flow chart to answer the questions.

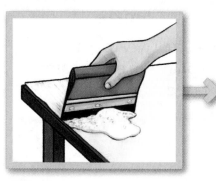

Step 1
Cloth is added to the cover of the ball to make it strong.

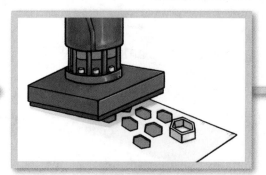

Step 2
Thirty–two shaped panels are punched out.

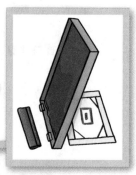

Step 3
A logo is stamped on one panel.

Step 4
Liquid rubber is formed into a balloon to go inside the ball.

Step 5
A worker stitches the panels together.

Step 6
The ball is complete.

1. What is the first step in making a soccer ball? _____

_____

2. How many panels are punched out? _____

3. What goes inside the ball? _____

4. How many people sew the panels for one ball together? _____

HERITAGE STUDIES

Landform

A **landform** is a certain shape of land on the earth.

Write the name of each landform.

hill
island
mountain
peninsula
plain

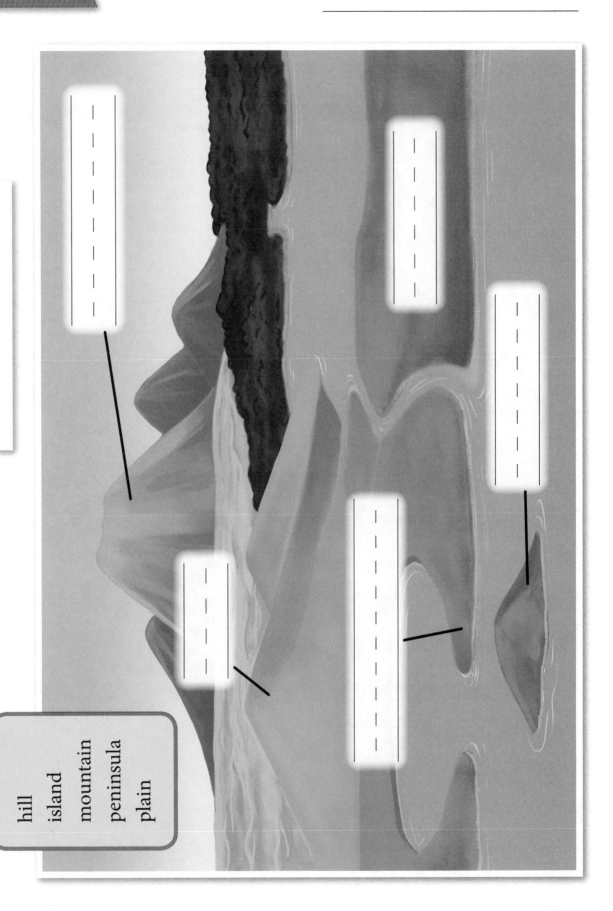

_____

- - - - - - - - - - - - - - - - -

_____

Landform Map

You can find different types of land and water on a **landform map**.

Draw a line to the word that completes the sentence.

1. A ____ might be long and narrow.

2. A ____ might be wide and round.

3. A ____ is water that is partly surrounded by land.

lake

gulf

river

Write the name of each body of water.

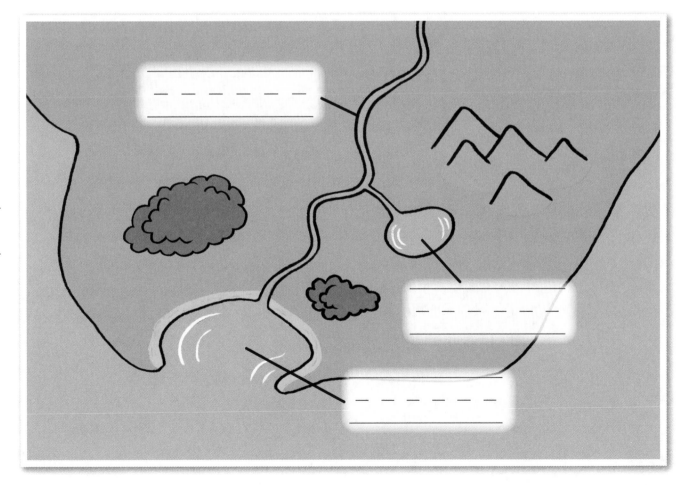

Make a travel flyer for Crater Lake National Park.
You may use your book.

Follow the steps to make a travel map.

1. Draw the outline of a state you have visited.

2. Write the name of the state.

3. Mark the town you visited with a dot.

4. Write the name of the town.

5. Draw a landform and body of water.

6. Draw a map key.

7. Write about your trip.

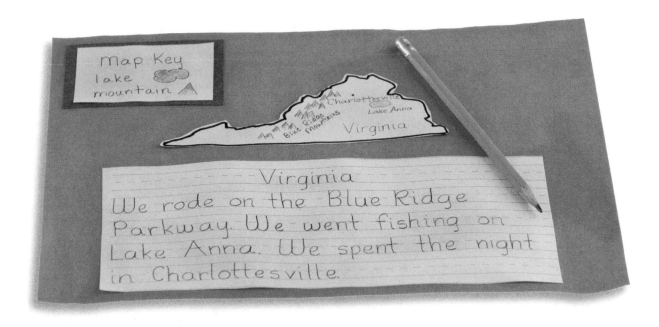

Mark the facts about each country. You may use your book.

Canada

Canada	Mexico	This country
		is north of the United States.
		is south of the United States.
		is one of the largest countries.
		has silver and gold as natural resources.
		has many visitors who enjoy fishing and hunting.

Mexico

_____

_ _ _ _ _ _ _ _ _ _ _ _ ⭐

Mark the correct answer.

1. God planned for people to fill ____ of the world.

   ⭕ part   ⭕ all

2. God wants us to ____ the earth.

   ⭕ care for   ⭕ litter

Circle the correct picture.

3. This family lives
   in a cold region.

4. This is a natural resource
   that God gives people to use.

5. This is the weather
   in a hot climate.

6. This job is being done
   in a cold climate.

Use the map to find the landforms and bodies of water.

7. Color the mountains brown.

8. Color the lake blue.

9. Color the island green.

10. Trace the river red.

Use the map to find America's neighbors.

11. Color the country north of the United States red.

12. Color the country south of the United States purple.

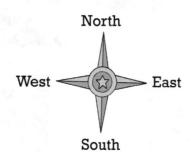

HERITAGE STUDIES

Trace the way to North America. Glue the pictures on the map.

Home

Tower

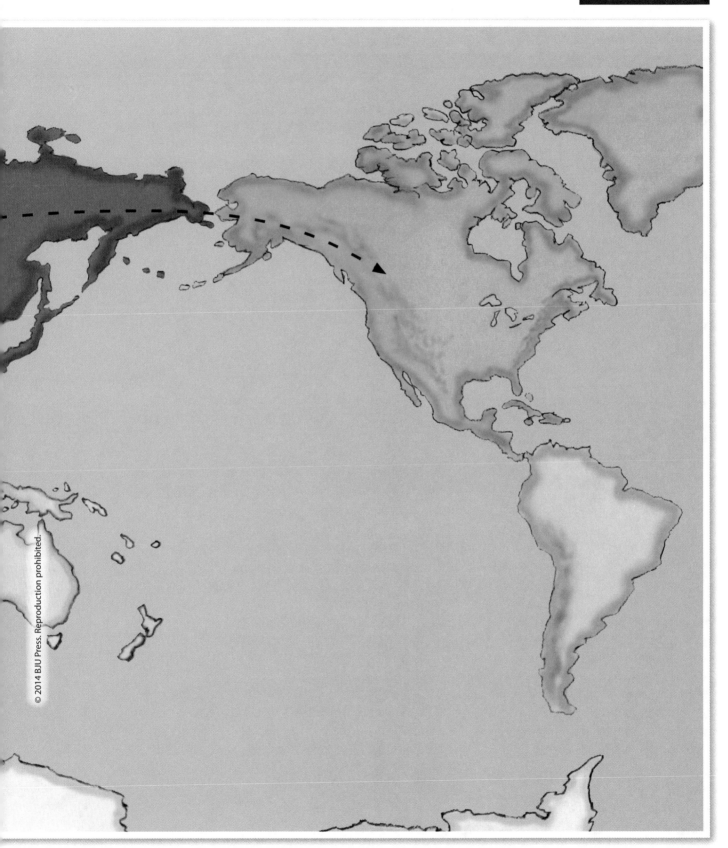

Using Natural Resources

Circle the Iroquois people who are wisely using a natural resource.

Natural Resources

A **natural resource** is something in nature that God gives people to use, like land, water, and animals.

Native American Artifacts

Glue below the artifact the picture of the natural resource it was made from.

Glue the picture of where the natural resource was found.

Artifact

An **artifact** is an object left behind from people long ago.

	Iroquois	Calusa	Mayas
Artifact			
Natural Resource			
Where the Natural Resource Was Found			

Cut along the solid lines.

- - - - - - - - - - - - - - - - - -

- - - - - - - - - - - - - - - - - -

Begin at the ★ and draw the route the Vikings took from Europe to North America.
Begin at the X and draw the route Columbus took from Europe to North America.

EUROPE

Italy

Spain

AFRICA

Portugal

Iceland

ATLANTIC
OCEAN

Greenland

Newfoundland

Bahamas

Canada

NORTH
AMERICA

Florida

Different Cultures

Culture

A **culture** is a way of life.

Write a sentence telling how the cultures are the same.

_ _ _ _ _ _ _ _ _ _ _ _ _ _ _ _

_ _ _ _ _ _ _ _ _ _ _ _ _ _ _ _

Write sentences telling how the shelters are different.

_ _ _ _ _ _ _ _ _ _ _ _ _ _ _ _

_ _ _ _ _ _ _ _ _ _ _ _ _ _ _ _

Write sentences telling how the clothing is different.

_____

_____

_____

_____

_____

Write a sentence telling why you think the Europeans did not treat the Native Americans well.

_____

_____

_____

_____

HERITAGE ❷ STUDIES

Number the events in the order in which they happened.

The ships sailed into the bay.

Pocahontas became a Christian.

John Smith made friends.

The men built a fort.

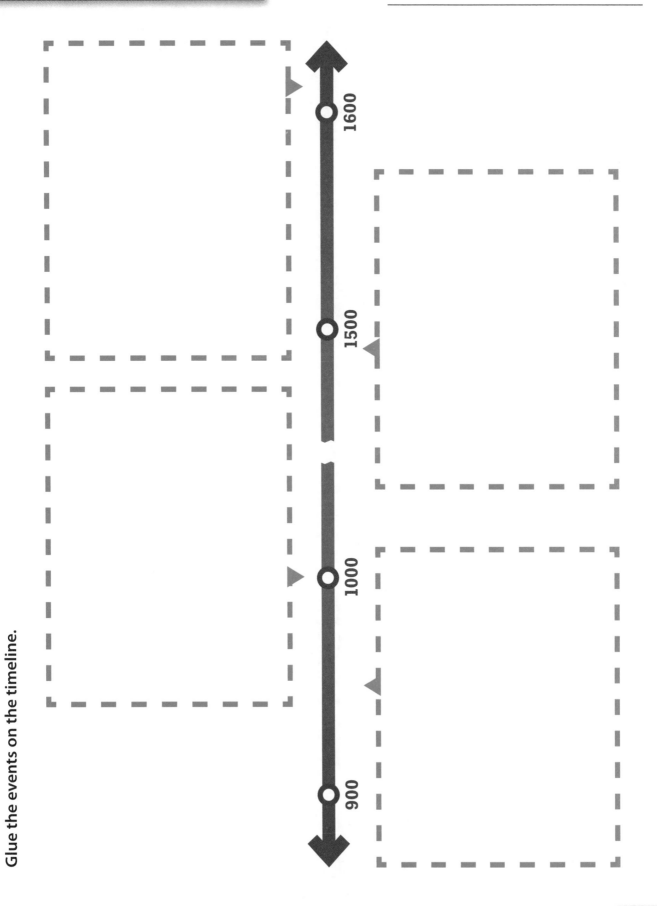

Glue the events on the timeline.

1600

1500

1000

900

Exploring Our Past

Cut out the events for the timeline.

1000 Ericson

Before **1000** Native Americans

1492 Columbus

1607 Jamestown

_____

_ ★

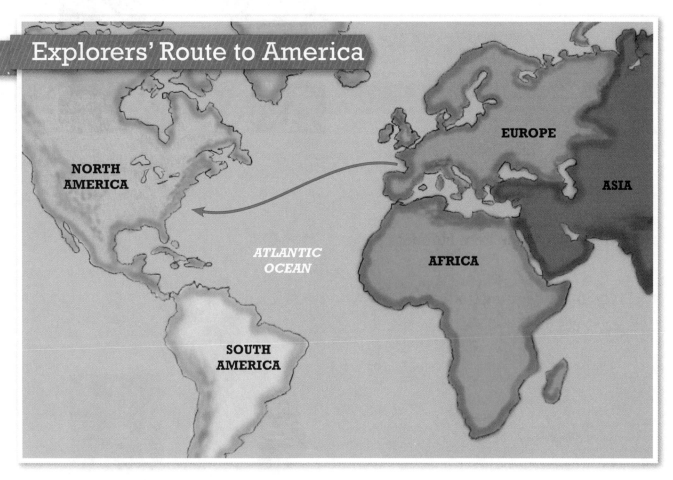

Explorers' Route to America

EUROPE

ASIA

NORTH
AMERICA

ATLANTIC
OCEAN

AFRICA

SOUTH
AMERICA

Use the map to answer the questions.

_____

_ _ _ _ _ _ _ _ _ _ _ _ _ _ _ _ _ _ _ _

1. From what continent did the explorers start? _____

_____

_ _ _ _ _ _ _ _ _ _ _ _ _ _ _ _ _ _ _ _

2. What continent were the explorers looking for? _____

_____

_ _ _ _ _ _ _ _ _ _ _ _ _ _ _ _ _ _ _ _

3. What continent did the explorers find? _____

4. What ocean did the explorers cross on the route to North America?
    _____

    _

    _____

Mark the correct picture.

5. Who were the first Americans? ◯

6. Which man came from Europe? ◯ ◯

7. Who made clothing from resources in the woods? ◯ ◯

8. Which doll is a Native American artifact? ◯ ◯

Number the events in the order in which they happened.

9.

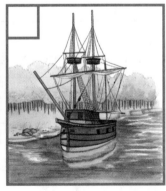
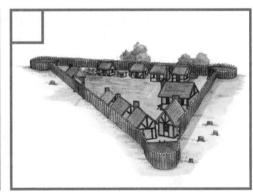

_____

_ _ _ _ _ _ _ _ _ _ _ _ _

_____

Glue the events on the timeline.

10.

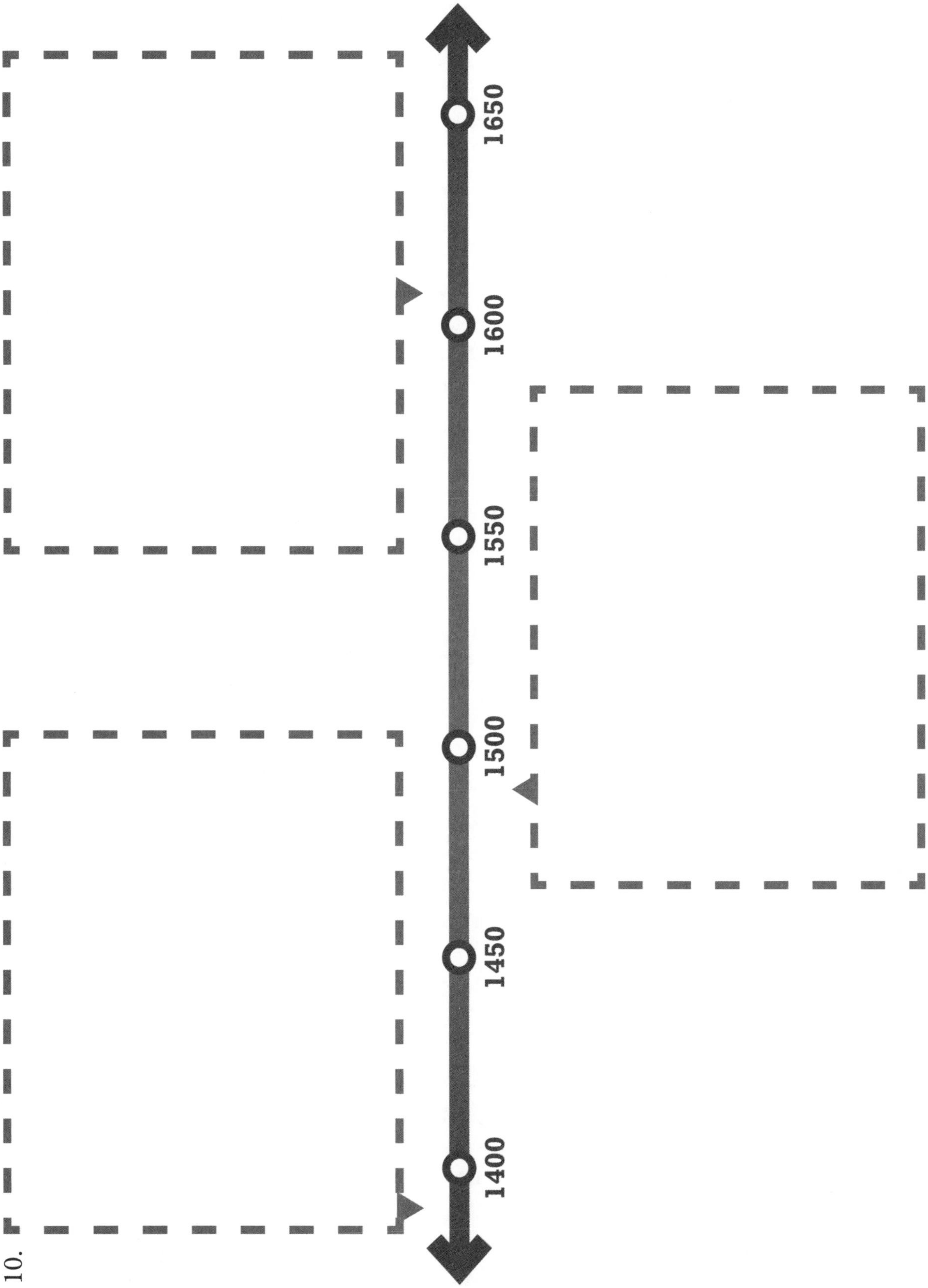

1650

1600

1550

1500

1450

1400

HERITAGE STUDIES ②

Chapter 5 Review

Cut out the events for the timeline.

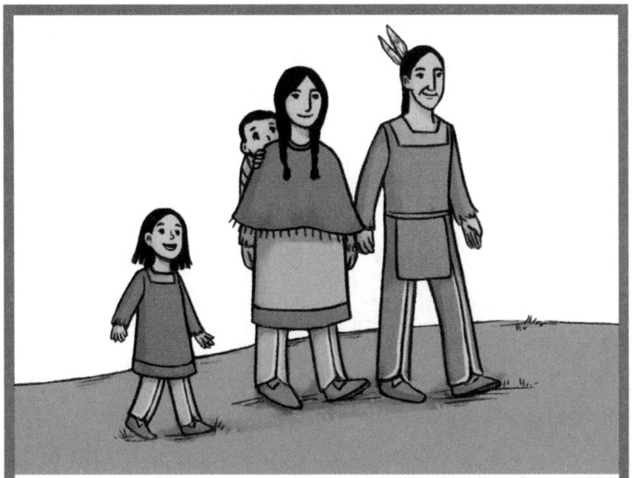

Native Americans

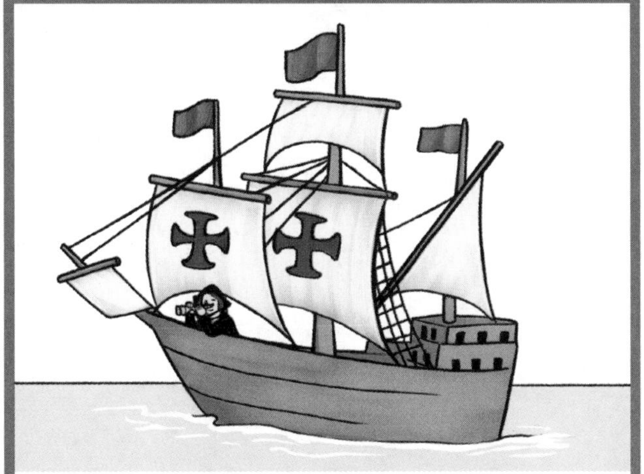

Columbus

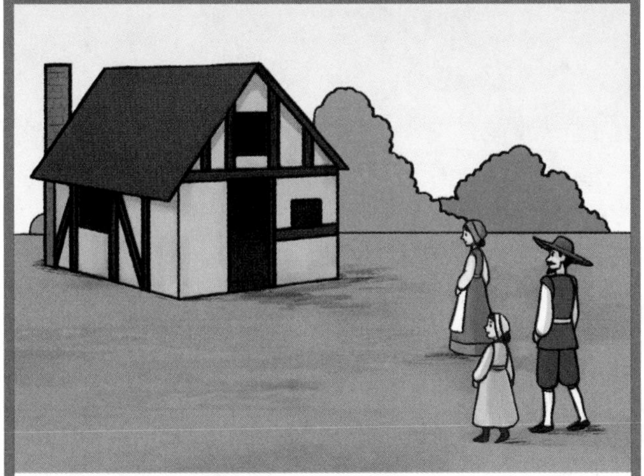

Jamestown

Draw a line to show the *Mayflower*'s path from England to America.

The *Mayflower*'s Path

Religion

Religion is a person's belief about where he came from, how to worship, and how to live.

Draw a line from the word to the correct picture.

> *Mayflower* Pilgrims Mayflower Compact

Cross out the belief that is *not* true of religion.

belief about how to live

belief about how to worship

belief about where to live

belief about where you came from

Mark the correct answer.

1. What was the name of the Pilgrims' colony?
   - ○ Plymouth
   - ○ Jamestown

2. What was the first winter in Plymouth like?
   - ○ plenty to eat
   - ○ not enough to eat

3. How did Squanto help the Pilgrims?
   - ○ showed them how to grow crops
   - ○ taught them to read the Bible

4. Who was the governor of Plymouth?
   - ○ Squanto
   - ○ William Bradford

5. Who was invited to the first Thanksgiving?
   - ○ Indians
   - ○ the king of England

Write about how you celebrate Thanksgiving.

Massachusetts Bay

Mark what is true about the Pilgrims, Puritans, or both.

	Pilgrims	Puritans
1. wanted to obey God		
2. wrote the Mayflower Compact		
3. settled in Massachusetts Bay		
4. settled in Plymouth		

Write three facts about John Winthrop.
You may use your book.

New England Colonies

Number the events in the order in which they happened.

_____ Roger Williams was a preacher in Massachusetts.

_____ Roger Williams started Rhode Island.

_____ Roger Williams left Massachusetts and went to live with some Indians.

Color the map.

1. Color Massachusetts red.

2. Color Rhode Island purple.

3. Color New Hampshire yellow.

4. Color Connecticut blue.

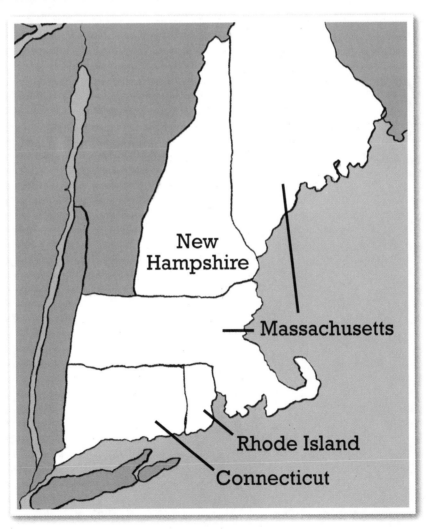

‾‾‾‾‾‾‾‾‾‾‾‾‾‾‾‾‾‾‾

Draw a line to match each New England family member to his or her job.

Father

Children

Mother

worked on a farm or at a trade

cared for the children, the home, and garden

did some of the same jobs as their parents

Trade

A **trade** is a job that takes special skill.

Circle what is true about worship services in the New England colonies.

where the people met	meetinghouse	homes
what the people sang	their own songs	the Psalms
the day they met	Saturday	Sunday

Draw arrows to show how New England colonists used a natural resource.

HERITAGE STUDIES

Schools in New England

Mark what is true about each kind of school in the New England colonies.

	Dame School	Grammar School	College
children taught in a woman's home			
Harvard			
Greek, Latin, math			
hornbook			
for young men who wanted to be ministers			
boys only			
learned about the Bible			

Write two facts about each New England poet. You may use your book.

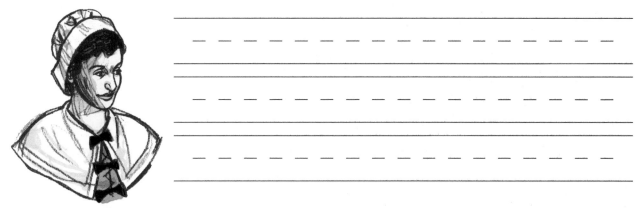

Anne Bradstreet

Phillis Wheatley

The Great Awakening

Draw a line from the phrase to the preacher it describes.

The Great Awakening

People in the colonies returned to God during the **Great Awakening**.

saw the great need in the churches

told the Indians about God's love

had a church in Massachusetts

traveled and preached for four years

died when he was a young man

Jonathan Edwards

David Brainerd

Answer the questions.

> Jonathan Edwards   David Brainerd   the Great Awakening

1. What was the return to God called in the colonies?

   ‗ ‗ ‗ ‗ ‗ ‗ ‗ ‗ ‗ ‗ ‗ ‗ ‗ ‗ ‗ ‗ ‗

2. Which preacher warned people in churches about their sin?

   ‗ ‗ ‗ ‗ ‗ ‗ ‗ ‗ ‗ ‗ ‗ ‗ ‗ ‗ ‗ ‗ ‗

3. Which preacher preached to the Indians about God's love?

   ‗ ‗ ‗ ‗ ‗ ‗ ‗ ‗ ‗ ‗ ‗ ‗ ‗ ‗ ‗ ‗ ‗

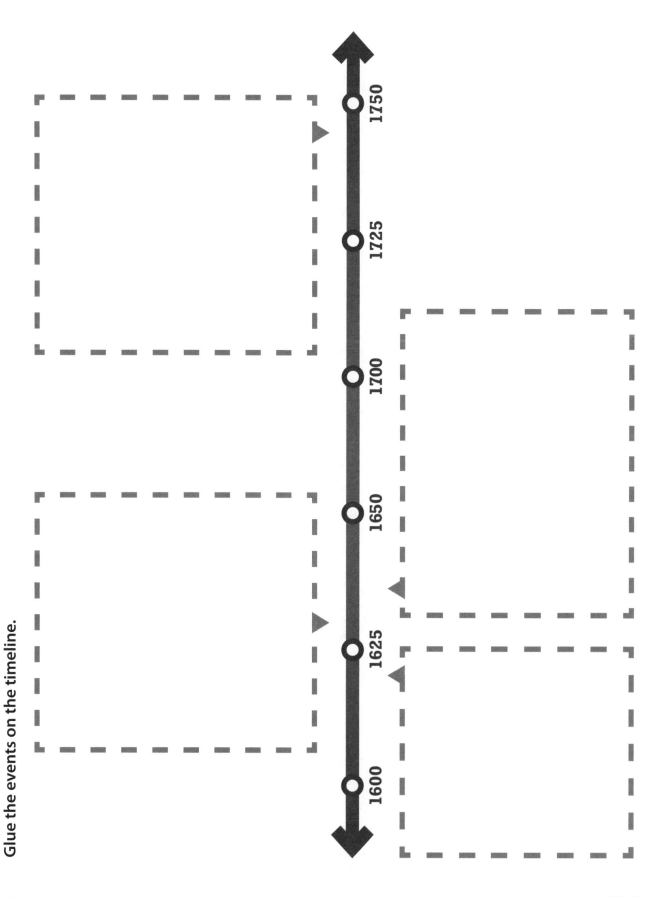

Glue the events on the timeline.

Exploring Our Past

Cut out the events for the timeline.

1630 Massachusetts Bay

1740s Great Awakening

1620 Plymouth

1636 Harvard College

Mark the correct answer.

1. Many people came to ____ to live the way God wanted them to live.

   ○ New England   ○ Jamestown

2. The ____ were a group of people that settled in Massachusetts Bay.

   ○ Indians   ○ Puritans

3. ____ is a person's belief about where he came from, how to worship, and how to live.

   ○ Religion   ○ Education

4. The Puritans taught their children to read the ____.

   ○ newspaper   ○ Bible

Draw a line to match the phrase with the correct picture.

5. the First Thanksgiving

6. a New England meetinghouse

7. a hornbook

8. trade in New England

Number the events in the order in which they happened.

Name a body of water important in settling New York.

The Island & the Harbor

Follow the directions.

1. You are a trader wanting furs. Use a red crayon to draw a route where you might find furs for trade.

2. You are a soldier protecting Manhattan Island. Use a blue crayon to draw a circle around the island.

3. You are a fisherman on Manhattan. Use a green crayon to show where you might find fish.

4. You are a ship captain staying on Manhattan. Use a black or brown crayon to show where you dock your ship.

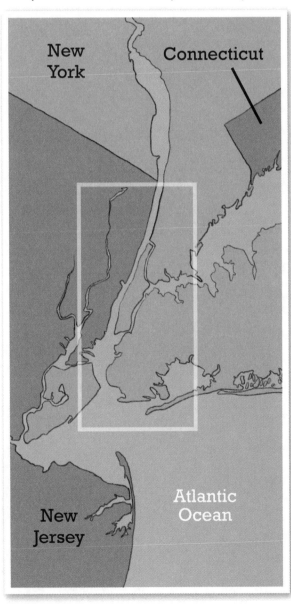

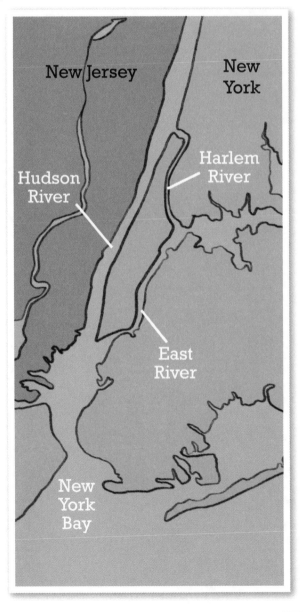

Pennsylvania

Mark the correct answer.

1. The Quakers trusted in the ____ more than the Bible.

   ○ inner light   ○ Church of England

2. The Quakers were ____ in England.

   ○ treated well   ○ not treated well

3. The king of England gave William Penn's family land in ____.

   ○ England   ○ America

4. William Penn paid the ____ for the land.

   ○ Indians   ○ Quakers

5. William Penn made ____ a place of religious freedom.

   ○ New England   ○ Pennsylvania

Circle the name of those who had religious freedom in Pennsylvania.

English   Dutch   Swedish   German

Design a city.

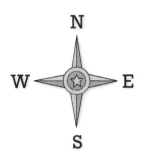

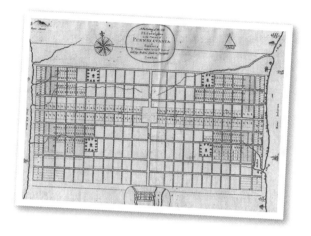

The City of Brotherly Love

Cut along the solid lines.

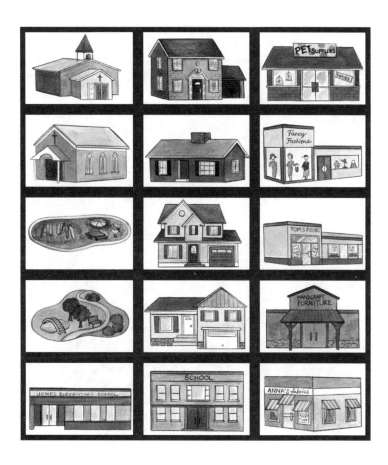

Put an *X* on Europe. Circle the middle colonies.
Draw a line from Europe to the middle colonies.

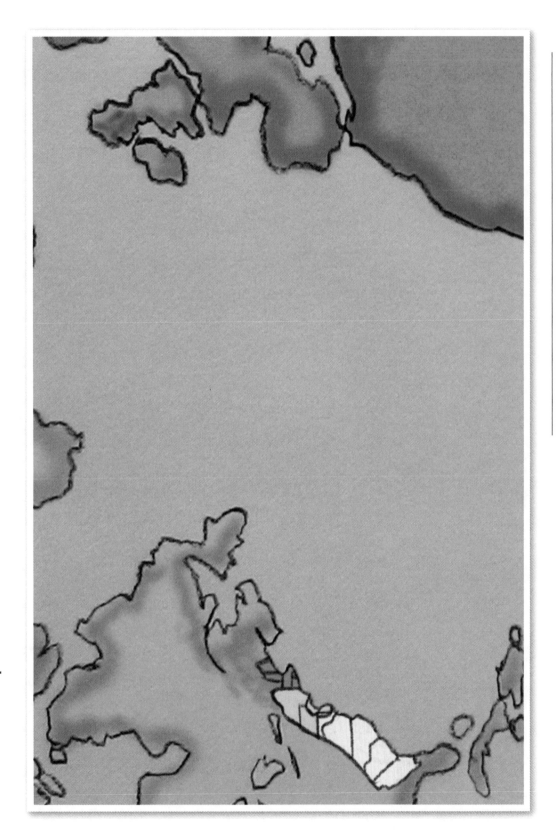

People from many different countries came to the _____.

Glue the pictures in the order in which the events happened.

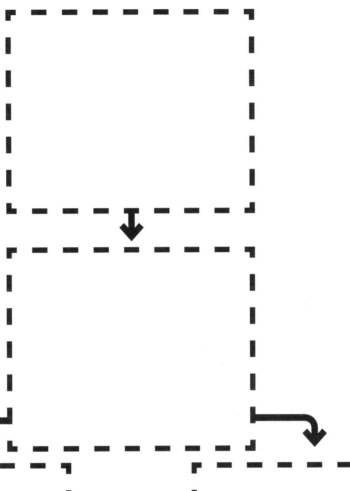

Grain was sold to the colonies.   Grain was shipped to Europe.

Who bought grain from the middle colonies? _____

_____

Cut along the solid lines.

Melting Pot of People

Write a sentence telling about the different people in the middle colonies.
The first sentence has been done for you.

Swedish

Swedish children found shellfish for wampum.

English and Indian

Dutch

German

———————————————

– – – – – – – – – – – – –

———————————————

Glue the events on the timeline.

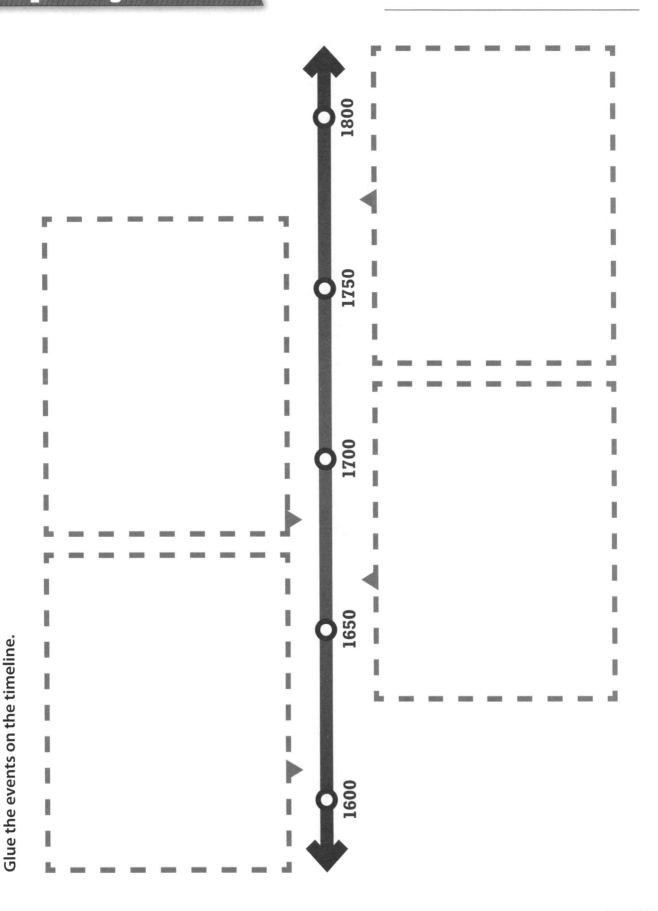

1800

1750

1700

1650

1600

Cut out the events for the timeline.

1609 Henry Hudson

1664 New York

1682 Pennsylvania

1776 Delaware

‑‑‑‑‑‑‑‑‑‑‑‑‑‑

Circle the correct answer.

1. A colony in the middle colonies

   Massachusetts   Pennsylvania

2. A job in the middle colonies

   farming   whaling

3. A boy wanting to learn a trade

   apprentice   pastor

4. A leader of the middle colonies

   William Bradford   William Penn

Mark the correct answer.

5. William Penn made Pennsylvania a place of religious ___.

   ◯ freedom   ◯ laws

6. People from many countries came to the ___ colonies.

   ◯ New England   ◯ middle

7. People in the middle colonies made ___ with the Indians.

   ◯ enemies   ◯ friends

8. People in the middle colonies had ___ jobs.

   ◯ different   ◯ the same

Number the events in the order in which they happened.

9.

Use the map to find the answers.

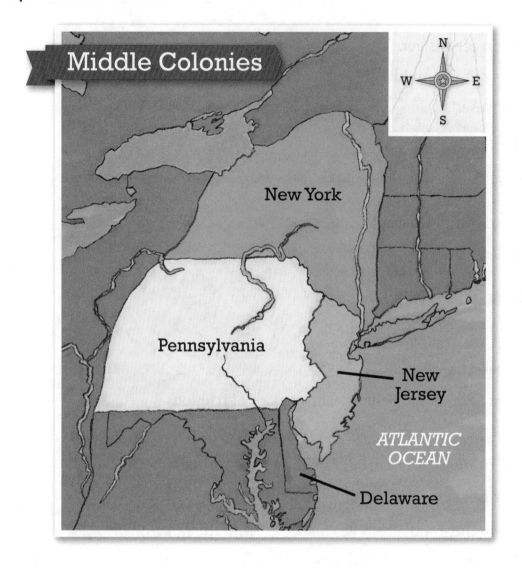

10. What is the name of the map? _____

11. Which colony is red? _____

12. Name the ocean. _____

13. What colony is north of Pennsylvania? _____

14. Circle the middle colonies on the map.

Virginia & Maryland

Circle _V_ for Virginia or _M_ for Maryland.

Virginia

Maryland

V   M   1. had the first colony in the new world to last

V   M   2. was a safe place for Catholics to live and worship

V   M   3. started on land given to George Calvert

V   M   4. formed the House of Burgesses to make laws

V   M   5. made Jamestown its capital

V   M   6. had a city called Saint Mary's

Write the word to complete the sentence.

bad

Indians

Tobacco

7. _____ became the main crop grown in Virginia.

8. The colonists had learned about tobacco from the _____.

9. Some people believed smoking tobacco was _____ for a person's health.

The Carolinas

Draw a line to the matching picture.

| indigo | plantation | port |

Write the term to complete the sentence.

| Carolina | Eliza Pinckney | rice | two |

1. _____ learned how to grow indigo.

2. Eight men named their land in America _____.

3. The warm, wet climate in Carolina was good for growing _____.

4. Carolina split into _____ southern colonies called North Carolina and South Carolina.

Draw a line from the phrase to the man it describes.

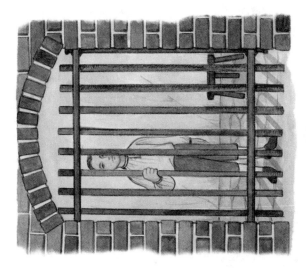

James Oglethorpe

had a friend who died in prison

had to go to prison

owed money to someone else

started a colony called Georgia
where debtors could live and work

made laws against slavery

could not work to earn money
while in prison

A debtor

Southern Colonies

Color the map.

1. Color Virginia red.

2. Color Maryland blue.

3. Color North Carolina yellow.

4. Color South Carolina purple.

5. Color Georgia orange.

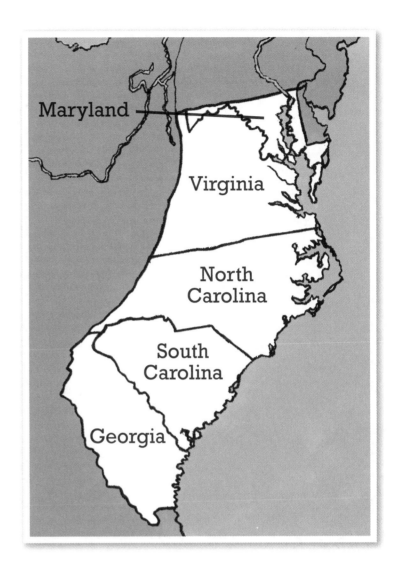

Use the map to answer the questions.

_____

_ _ _ _ _ _ _ _ _

_____   6. Which colony is farthest south?
_____

_ _ _ _ _ _ _ _

_____   7. How many southern colonies touch the Atlantic
                                Ocean?

_____

_ _ _ _ _ _ _ _ _

_____   8. Which colony is farthest north?
_____

_ _ _ _ _ _ _ _

_____   9. Which southern colony is the smallest?

Cut along the solid lines and glue the pictures in place to make
a plantation.

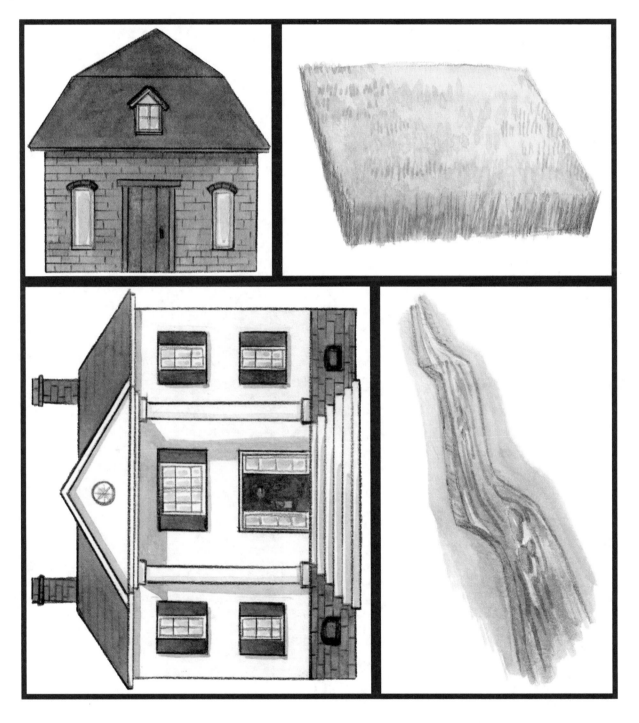

Cut along the solid lines and glue the pictures in place to make a plantation.

Plantation Slaves

_____

_ _ _ _ _ _ _ _ _ _

Mark the correct answer.

1. Where did most slaves work?

   ○ in the fields   ○ in a bank

2. Where did slaves live?

   ○ in apartments   ○ in cabins

3. What were slaves given for their work?

   ○ a lot of money   ○ food, clothing, and a place to live

4. Where did most slaves come from?

   ○ West Africa   ○ England

5. What job did some children of slaves do?

   ○ pulled weeds   ○ plowed fields

Circle the phrase in each row that is true about slaves.

6. treated other slaves like family   always lived with their family

7. cooked plain foods   cooked special dishes

8. many became Christians   many became Catholics

9. sang only funny songs   sang about Jesus and the freedom He gives

Mark the correct answer.

1. From which country did the first settlers in the southern colonies come?

   ○ Spain   ○ England

2. What were members of the Church of England called?

   ○ Anglicans   ○ Quakers

3. Who were not treated the same as their owners?

   ○ slaves   ○ colonists

4. What were the groups of Christian French colonists called?

   ○ Pilgrims   ○ Huguenots

Circle the pictures that show what skills the Huguenots brought to the colonies.

How were children taught in the southern colonies?

_____

_____

_____

_____

_____

Exploring Our Past

Glue the events on the timeline.

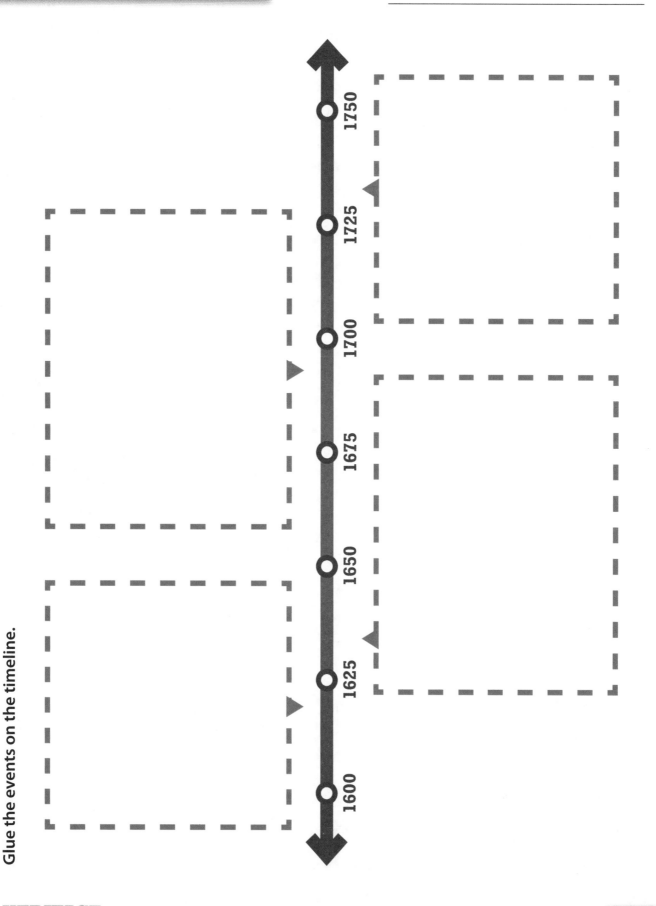

Cut out the events for the timeline.

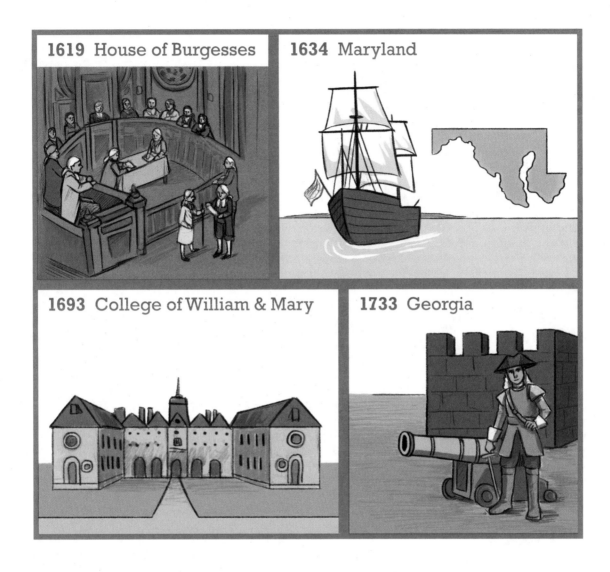

1619 House of Burgesses

1634 Maryland

1693 College of William & Mary

1733 Georgia

The Colonies

Look at the map on page 152 in your book.
Mark the correct answers with an *X*.

	New England Colonies	Middle Colonies	Southern Colonies
Virginia			
Georgia			
Massachusetts			
Rhode Island			
New York			
Pennsylvania			

Use the chart on page 153 to answer the questions.

1. Which region was mostly Puritan?

2. Which region had dame schools?

3. Which region had English colonists and African slaves?

4. In which regions was farming important?

Use the map to answer the questions.

The Thirteen Colonies

1. What does the map show?
   - ○ the United States of America
   - ○ the Thirteen Colonies

2. Which colony is south of Virginia?
   - ○ Georgia
   - ○ Pennsylvania

3. Which ocean is along the east coast of the colonies?
   - ○ Atlantic Ocean
   - ○ Pacific Ocean

4. Which colony is the farthest north?
   - ○ North Carolina
   - ○ Massachusetts

Massachusetts

New Hampshire

New York

Pennsylvania

Rhode Island

Connecticut

New Jersey

Delaware

Virginia

Maryland

North Carolina

South Carolina

Georgia

Atlantic Ocean

Write the word to complete the sentence.

Catholics   laws   plantations   Rice

_____
— — — — — — — — — — — —
_____

5. The Virginia House of Burgesses made ____ for the people.

_____
— — — — — — — — — — —
_____

6. The colony of Maryland was a safe place for ____ to settle.

_____
— — — — — — — — — — —
_____

7. The very large farms in Carolina were called ____.

_____
— — — — — — — — — — — —
_____

8. ____ was grown on many farms in the southern colonies.

Mark the correct answer.

9. Why did James Oglethorpe start a colony in Georgia?
   - ○ He wanted to give debtors a place to live and work.
   - ○ He wanted to free the people from jail.

10. What did southern farmers call the crop they grew to make money?
    - ○ wheat crop
    - ○ cash crop
    - ○ fur trade
    - ○ shipping industry

11. What kind of worker did most plantations depend on?
    - ○ a factory worker
    - ○ an immigrant
    - ○ a slave
    - ○ an apprentice

12. Where did the children in the southern colonies have school?
    - ○ in a school building
    - ○ in a church
    - ○ at home
    - ○ in a dame school

HERITAGE STUDIES

The French & Indian War

Compare the French to the English.
Use page 157 to complete the chart.

Why did the war begin?

The French wanted . . .	The British wanted . . .
_ _ _ _ _ _ _ _ _	_ _ _ _ _ _ _ _ _
_____	_____
_____	_____
_____	_____
_____	_____

British Soldier

Who fought on each side?

French side	British side
_____	_ _ _ _ _ _ _ _ _
_ _ _ _ _ _ _ _ _	_____
_____	_____
_____	_____
_____	_____

French Fur Trader

How many years did the war last? _____
_____

Who won the war? _____

HERITAGE STUDIES

Look at the pictures. Use page 158 to complete the sentence.

First	Next	Last

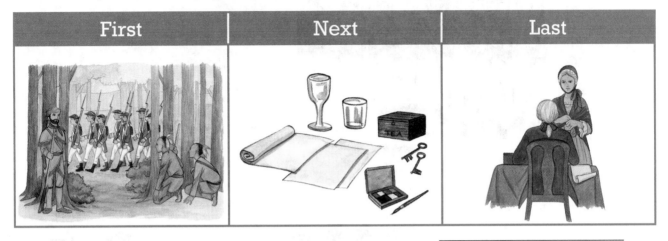

After the French and Indian War, the colonists had to pay _____.

Tax

A **tax** is money paid
to the government.

Use page 159 to write a sentence about taxes showing two points of view.

Different Points of View

I will

_____

_____

I will

_____

_____

Use page 160 to write a sentence telling about the Boston massacre.

First

Next

Last

_____

_ _

_____

_ _

_____

HERITAGE STUDIES

Write a sentence telling how some colonists acted toward the tax on tea.

Some colonists
acted this way.

_____

_____

_____

_____

Draw a picture. Write a sentence.

How I would act
toward a tax on tea

_____

_____

_____

_____

Write a sentence telling how the colonists acted toward the closing of the port of Boston.

The colonists reacted to the closing of the port of Boston in two ways.

The Loyalists _____

_____

_____

The Patriots _____

_____

_____

Loyalist

Patriot

Which way do you think was right? Why?

_____

_____

_____

_____

HERITAGE STUDIES

Headed for War

_____
_ _ _ _ _ _ _ _ _ _ _ _ _ _

Glue the pictures in the order in which the events happened.
Write a sentence describing each picture.

First	Next	Last

Headed for War

Cut along the solid lines.

Declaring Independence

George Washington

Declare
Declare means "to make known."

Independence
Independence means "to be free from another country."

Thomas Jefferson

Write details from pages 167–169.

Detail

_ _

_ _

Detail

_ _

_ _

Retell the main idea.

Main Idea

_ _

_ _

The Revolutionary War

Use pages 170–172 to write a sentence about the war.

The American army _____

1. _____

_____

The British army _____

2. _____

_____

British Soldier

George Washington _____

3. _____

_____

Baron von Steuben _____

4. _____

_____

American Soldier

battle _____

_____

5. _____

_____

_____

_____

6. Do you think the American soldiers were brave? Why?

_____

_____

_____

_____

Write a question about the war. Ask a friend the question.

_____

_____

_____

_____

HERITAGE STUDIES

Timeline

A **timeline** is a chart that shows events in the order in which they happened.

Revolutionary
War begins
1775

British surrender
at Yorktown
1781

1760   1763   1770   1773   1776   1780   1790
French and
Indian War ends

Boston
Tea Party

Declaration of
Independence

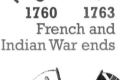

Use the timeline to answer the questions.

1. How many events are on the timeline? _____

2. Which event started in 1775? _____

3. In what year did the French and Indian War end? _____

4. What year does the timeline begin? _____

5. What year does the timeline end? _____

6. What happened in 1773? _____

7. What does the timeline show? _____

_____

8. Did the signing of the Declaration of Independence happen before or after

the British surrender at Yorktown? _____

Make a timeline of your life.

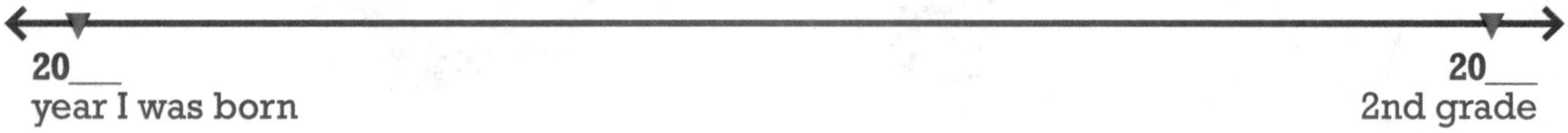

20___
year I was born

20___
2nd grade

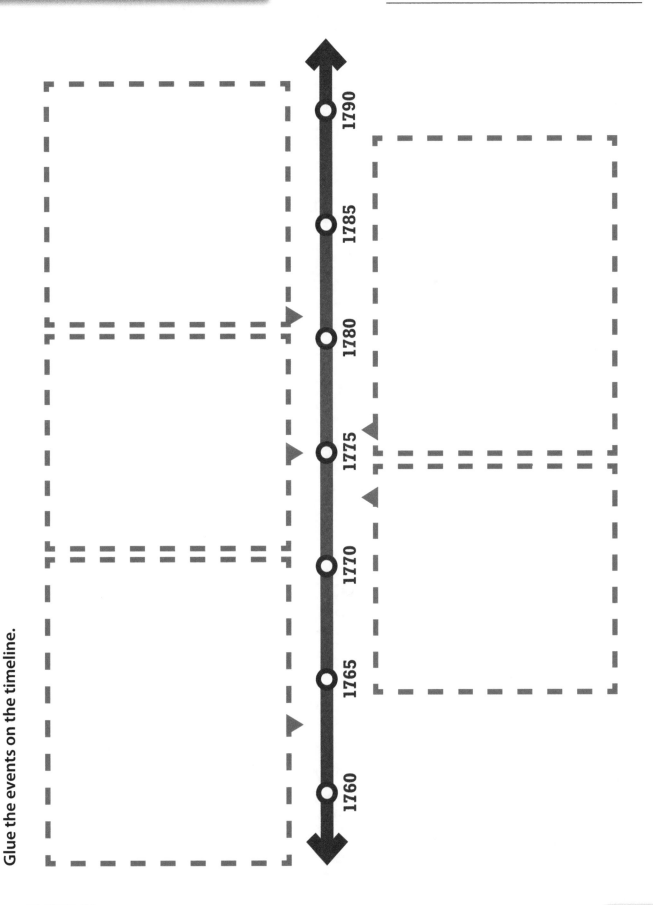

Glue the events on the timeline.

1790

1785

1780

1775

1770

1765

1760

Cut out the events for the timeline.

1773 Boston Tea Party

1776 Declaration of Independence

1781 British surrender at Yorktown

1775 Revolutionary War begins

1763 French & Indian War ends

Circle the correct answer.

1. What war gave Great Britain control over North America?

   Revolutionary War   French and Indian War

2. What tax made the colonists angry?

   tea tax   coffee tax

3. What paper did the leaders write to declare their rights and freedom?

   the Constitution   the Declaration of Independence

4. Who was the leader of the American army?

   Thomas Jefferson   George Washington

Write the word to complete the sentence.

> British   Independence   Tax

5. _____ is money paid to the government.

6. _____ is to be free from another country.

7. The _____ were people who lived in England,
   Scotland, Ireland, and Wales.

Mark the answer that completes the sentence.

8. Colonists dressed as Indians threw tea _____.

   ○ into the Boston harbor   ○ on the Lexington Green

9. Patriots were willing to _____.

   ○ fight for the king   ○ fight for independence

10. The British army surrendered to the _____.

    ○ Spanish at Yorktown   ○ Americans at Yorktown

Write a sentence telling how the Revolutionary War has made your life different today.

_____

_____

_____

_____

HERITAGE STUDIES

Match the definition to the correct term.

_____ 1. the war between the colonists and the British

_____ 2. a new plan of government

_____ 3. the leaders of each colony who met and
made decisions

> A. Articles of Confederation
> B. Continental Congress
> C. Revolutionary War

Write the questions in the speech bubble.

Pretend you were living in a colony after the war was over. How would things change? Write two questions you would ask your parents about the future.

Circle the powers the new country would need.

power to tax

power to raise an army

power to choose a king

power to fight wars

power to settle land problems

Mark the correct answer.

1. The city where the leaders met was called ____.

   ○ Charleston   ○ Philadelphia

2. The state that did not send a man to work on the Constitution was ____.

   ○ Rhode Island   ○ New York

3. The ____ is one of the most important writings in America's history.

   ○ Constitution   ○ Articles of Confederation

4. ____ was in charge of the meetings.

   ○ John Dickinson   ○ George Washington

The Great Compromise

Compromise

A **compromise** is a way to solve an argument so that the people on both sides are happy.

Roger Sherman

Write the word to complete the sentence.

control   equal   number   two   votes

1. The men could not agree on how many _____ each state should have.
   _____
   _ _ _ _ _

2. They did not want any one state to have too much _____ .
   _____
   _ _ _ _ _ _ _ _ _

3. There would be _____ groups of leaders who made laws.
   _____
   _ _ _ _ _

4. One group would have an _____ number of leaders from each state.
   _____
   _ _ _ _ _

5. In the other group, the number of leaders would be decided by the
   _____
   _ _ _ _ _ _ _
   _____ of people in each state.

Write the letter of the correct term to complete the sentence.

_____ 6. The _____ has an equal number of leaders from each state.

_____ 7. Roger Sherman's plan was called the _____.

_____ 8. The form of government that allows citizens to choose their leaders is called a _____.

_____ 9. The number of leaders in the _____ is decided by the number of people in each state.

A. Great Compromise

B. House

C. republic

D. Senate

HERITAGE STUDIES

The Constitution

Number the events in the order in which they happened.

_____ The leaders went back home to their states.

_____ The leaders signed the Constitution.

_____ The leaders met and worked on the Constitution for many months.

_____ The Constitution was adopted in 1789.

_____ New Hampshire accepted the Constitution.

_____ The Bill of Rights was added to the Constitution.

Write an idea for a new freedom you would like to have for your classroom or your playground. Ask three of your friends to agree to it and sign their names.

George Washington

Cut out the pictures of George Washington and put them in the correct order.

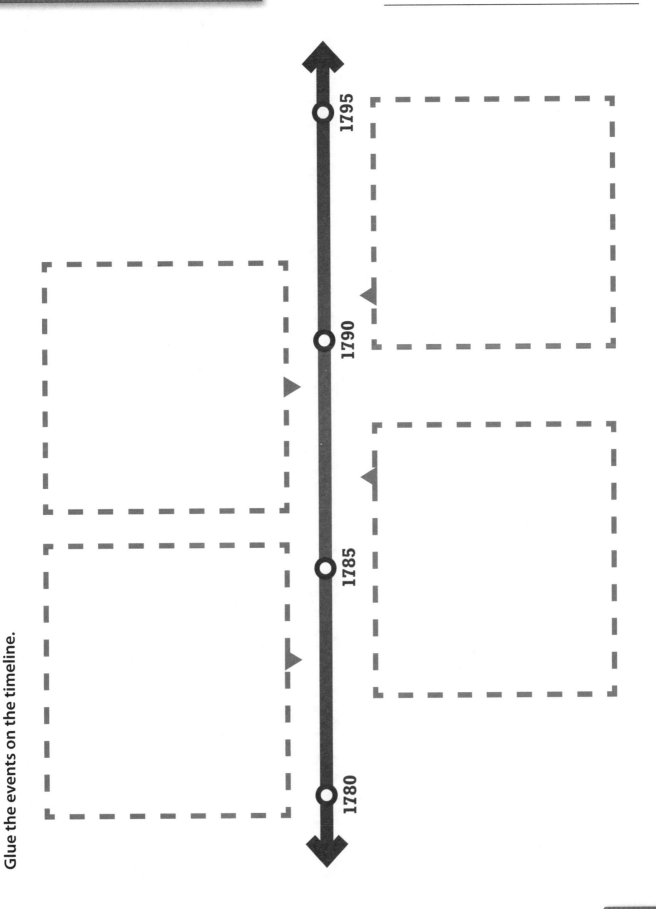

Glue the events on the timeline.

Cut along the solid lines.

1783 Treaty of Paris

1791 Bill of Rights

1787 Constitution

1789 George Washington becomes president

Match the definition to the correct term.

_____ 1. a way to solve an argument so that the people on both sides are happy

_____ 2. a plan for a new kind of government called a republic

_____ 3. a list of the people's freedoms added to the Constitution

A. Bill of Rights

B. compromise

C. Constitution

Mark the sentences that are true about George Washington.

○ He was in charge of the leaders at the meeting in Philadelphia.

○ He was known as the Great Compromiser.

○ He was the first president.

Number the events in the order in which they happened.

_____ George Washington became the first president.

_____ The Revolutionary War ended.

_____ The Constitution of the United States was written.

Write a sentence telling why you think George Washington was a good president.

_____

— — — — — — — — — — — — — — — — — —

_____

_____

— — — — — — — — — — — — — — — — — —

_____

_____

— — — — — — — — — — — — — — — — — —

Photograph Credits

19tl © iStockphoto.com/ Gregory Olsen; **19**r © iStockphoto.com/ Jay Lazarin; **19**bl, **32**tl, **32**tr, **32**c, **32**bl iStockphoto/Thinkstock; **29** Dave Kotinsky/Getty Images Entertainment/Getty Images; **32**tc © iStockphoto.com/Fred Froese; **32**cl George Doyle/Stockbyte/Thinkstock; **32**cr © iStockphoto.com/Lisa F. Young; **32**bc Creatas Images/Thinkstock; **32**br © iStockphoto.com/Enrico Fianchini; **47**tl "George Washington the first good president 1846" by Gilbert Stuart/Wikipedia/Public Domain; **47**tr, **54**cr © Gary Blakeley/Dreamstime.com; **47**cl Commons.wikimedia .org/New York Historical Society; **47**cr, **47**br, **54**tl, **54**tr, **54**cl, **54**bl, **54**br, **69**ctr, **143**c, Getty Images/iStockphoto/Thinkstock; **47**bl Library of Congress; **53** "Official Portrait of President Reagan 1981"/White House/Wikimedia/Public Domain; **65** BJU Photo Services; **69**tl Gorilla/Bigstock.com; **69**tr © iStockphoto.com/kristian sekulic; **69**ctl © Onizu3d/Dreamstime.com; **69**cbl Getty Images/Zoonar RF/ Thinkstock; **69**cbr Getty Images/Brand X/Thinkstock; **69**bl © iStockphoto.com/ Oliver Childs; **69**br Barbara Reddoch/Bigstock.com; **83**l Marilyn Angel Wynn/ Nativestock/Getty Images; **83**r age fotostock/SuperStock; **84**l Ira Block/National Geographic/Getty Images; **84**r © Nancy G Western Photography, Nancy Greifenhagen/Alamy; **92**tl © Sergei Bachlakov/Dreamstime.com; **92**tr Stephen Saks Photography/Alamy; **92**bl © iStockphoto.com/Loretta Hostettler; **92**br Christie's Images Ltd./ SuperStock; **123** Penn's Grid for Philadelphia/Public Domain; **143**l Wollwerth Imagery/Bigstock.com; **143**r Jeremy Woodhouse/The Image Bank/Getty Images; **191** "Roger Sherman" by Ralph Earl/Wikimedia Commons/Public Domain; **193** Constitution of the United States/Wikipedia/Public Domain